# DANCE, LITTLE ALLEIU, WITH ME

Words by Norman C. Habel
Pictures by Jim Roberts

A PURPLE PUZZLE TREE BOOK

COPYRIGHT © 1973 CONCORDIA PUBLISHING HOUSE, ST. LOUIS, MISSOURI
CONCORDIA PUBLISHING HOUSE LTD., LONDON, E. C. 1
MANUFACTURED IN THE UNITED STATES OF AMERICA
ALL RIGHTS RESERVED
ISBN 0-570-06549-6

Concordia Publishing House

On the day God made the morning,
orange sun and merry moon,
that's when angels rode the rainbows,
danced and sang this pretty tune:
Oh, dance, little Allelu, with me,
Allelu, Allelu!
Dance, little Allelu, with me,
round the purple puzzle tree.

Allelu was born that morning,
brightest angel in the sky.
When she danced, her wings would flutter
like a sparkling butterfly.
So dance, little Allelu, with me,
Allelu, Allelu!
Dance, little Allelu, with me,
round the purple puzzle tree.

That's true!
Allelu, the angel of joy,
led the dance with God
when He first made the world.

And Allelu was near the tomb of Jesus
when God raised up His Son,
to bring the world alive again
according to His puzzle plan.

You see, when Jesus died,
all the world died with Him.
They laid Him in a tomb
that was really like a cave,
and rolled a stone in front.
Later God sent Allelu
to sit beside that tomb,
ready to dance for joy.

Just as the orange light
crept into the sky that dawn,
the rocks began to roll around,
rumble, leap and dance about
like happy jumping beans.

Allelu dodged all the rocks
and flew up to the tomb.
Then she got an angel scare
to see two great big angels
standing guard right there
bright as the morning sun.

But Jesus Christ was gone.
He had risen from the dead.

So when the angels saw scared Allelu
they told her everything they knew
and danced a resurrection dance:

Today's the day God raised His Son,
made this world so bright and new.
Will you join the angels' dance?
Flowers, trees, and children do.

Oh, dance, little Allelu, with me,
Allelu, Allelu!
Dance, little Allelu, with me,
round the purple puzzle tree.

Soon after dawn some women came
to anoint the body of Jesus.
When they saw the dazzling angels there
the women's hearts were filled with fear,
and they fell down on the ground.

"Why seek the living among the dead?"
the dazzling angels said.
"He isn't here. He's risen."
Then Allelu stirred up their hearts
to remember Jesus' words,
that He would come to life again
according to God's puzzle plan.

They rushed away with Allelu
to tell the friends of Jesus,
but no one would believe them.

Peter the Rock and John His friend
raced off to see for themselves.
John ran faster than Rock, his friend,
but Rock was first inside.
And there upon the ground
were long linen cloths
they'd wrapped around their Lord
soon after He had died.

A few days later
Old Rock and his fishermen friends
went out to catch some fish,
but they couldn't catch a thing.

Then slowly close beside the shore
a Stranger came in sight.
"Catch any fish?" He yelled aloud.
"Not a blessed thing," they replied.
"Try the other side of the boat.
You'll catch a pile," the Stranger cried.

So they threw out the net
and started to pull
with a heave and a ho
and a yo-ho-ho.
What do you know?
They found themselves sitting
up to their necks with fish,
slipping, flipping,
flapping, slapping fish
in a slippery, sinking boat.

"It must be the Lord," said Peter with glee,
and jumped right in the lake
with half of his clothes half on
and swam straight back to shore.

Jesus broke a loaf of bread
and blessed the fish they ate.
They had their breakfast with the Lord,
just as we may do today.

Then Jesus said to Peter the Rock,
"Do you love Me now, My friend?"
"You know I love You, Lord," said Rock.
"Then feed My lambs," said Jesus.
"Tell the world the wonderful news
that I have risen from the grave
to free men from the fear of death."

If you had been around that morn
you might have seen upon that beach
the dance of Rock with Christ, his Lord,
when Allelu filled them with joy.
Would you like to sing along?:

Bright and early any morning
ask your Lord to dine with you.
Taste the joy He gave to Peter,
dance your day with Allelu.

Oh, dance, little Allelu, with me,
Allelu, Allelu!
Dance, little Allelu, with me
round the purple puzzle tree.

When the time had come for Christ
    to leave
He gathered all His faithful friends
on a mountain in Galilee.
"Go and tell the world," He said,
"I came to die and live for you.
Soon I'll send God's Spirit down,
His very secret power for men,
to help you spread God's love abroad
and keep your spirit free within."

Then softly, oh, so softly,
a cloud swept past the mountain,
and Jesus vanished from sight.
He went to be with God Himself,
which is everywhere there is.

A few weeks later at Pentecost
the disciples gathered again.
Then suddenly they all could hear,
"Whwhwhwhoooo! Whwhwhwheeee!"
A whistling wind came from the sky
and swirled around the room
where all the friends of Jesus stood.
It hovered there like music does,
filling all the space.

Then bright, red flames of fire
spun around inside the room
like fluttering bright, red wings.
They rested on the heads
of each of Jesus' friends.
The flames were signs of the Holy Spirit
that Jesus promised He would send.

Then all the friends of Jesus
began to speak of Christ, their Lord,
in many languages and ways
they'd never known before.

They told the world that God had come
in Jesus Christ, their Lord,
to be the answer and the key
of the puzzle plan of God
that grew and grew for years
like a purple puzzle tree.

For since the days of Adam and Eve,
Moses and David and John
and all, God's puzzle people
have been looking for the day
when God would set His people free
from the grip of sin and death.

Now that day was here!

For Jesus Christ the risen Lord
had come to dwell within our hearts
and give us all a special life,
a life that never dies,
a life that sets us free!

    So, dance, little Allelu with me,
    Allelu, Allelu!
    Dance, little Allelu with me,
    round the purple puzzle tree.

# OTHER TITLES

## SET I

WHEN GOD WAS ALL ALONE 56-1200
WHEN THE FIRST MAN CAME 56-1201
IN THE ENCHANTED GARDEN 56-1202
WHEN THE PURPLE WATERS CAME AGAIN 56-1203
IN THE LAND OF THE GREAT WHITE CASTLE 56-1204
WHEN LAUGHING BOY WAS BORN 56-1205
SET I LP RECORD 79-2200
SET I GIFT BOX (6 BOOKS, 1 RECORD) 56-1206

## SET II

HOW TRICKY JACOB WAS TRICKED 56-1207
WHEN JACOB BURIED HIS TREASURE 56-1208
WHEN GOD TOLD US HIS NAME 56-1209
IS THAT GOD AT THE DOOR? 56-1210
IN THE MIDDLE OF A WILD CHASE 56-1211
THIS OLD MAN CALLED MOSES 56-1212
SET II LP RECORD 79-2201
SET II GIFT BOX (6 BOOKS, 1 RECORD) 56-1213

## SET III

THE TROUBLE WITH TICKLE THE TIGER 56-1218
AT THE BATTLE OF JERICHO! HO! HO! 56-1219
GOD IS NOT A JACK-IN-A-BOX 56-1220
A LITTLE BOY WHO HAD A LITTLE FLING 56-1221
THE KING WHO WAS A CLOWN 56-1222
SING A SONG OF SOLOMON 56-1223
SET III LP RECORD 79-2202
SET III GIFT BOX (6 BOOKS, 1 RECORD) 56-1224

## SET IV

ELIJAH AND THE BULL-GOD BAAL 56-1225
LONELY ELIJAH AND THE LITTLE PEOPLE 56-1226
WHEN ISAIAH SAW THE SIZZLING SERAPHIM 56-1227
A VOYAGE TO THE BOTTOM OF THE SEA 56-1228
WHEN JEREMIAH LEARNED A SECRET 56-1229
THE CLUMSY ANGEL AND THE NEW KING 56-1230
SET IV LP RECORD 79-2203
SET IV GIFT BOX (6 BOOKS, 1 RECORD) 56-1231

## SET V

THE FIRST TRUE SUPER STAR 56-1242
A WILD YOUNG MAN CALLED JOHN 56-1243
THE DIRTY DEVIL AND THE CARPENTERS BOY 56-1244
WHEN JESUS DID HIS MIRACLES OF LOVE 56-1245
WHEN JESUS TOLD HIS PARABLES 56-1246
OLD ROCK THE FISHERMAN 56-1247
SET V LP RECORD 79-2204
SET V GIFT BOX 56-1248

## SET VI

WONDER BREAD FROM A BOY'S LUNCH 56-1249
WHEN JESUS RODE IN THE PURPLE PUZZLE
   PARADE 56-1250
WHEN JESUS' FRIENDS BETRAYED HIM 56-1251
THE DEEP DARK DAY WHEN JESUS DIED 56-1252
DANCE, LITTLE ALLELU, WITH ME 56-1253
THE KEY TO THE PURPLE PUZZLE TREE 56-1254
SET VI LP RECORD 79-2205
SET VI GIFT BOX 56-1255

the PURPLE PUZZLE TREE